IT'S EASY TO PLAY

KEANE
HOPES AND FEARS

Wise Publications
part of The Music Sales Group

London / New York / Paris / Sydney / Copenhagen / Berlin / Madrid / Tokyo

Published by
Wise Publications
14/15 Berners Street, London, W1T 3LJ, England.

Exclusive Distributors:
Music Sales Limited
Distribution Centre, Newmarket Road, Bury St Edmunds, Suffolk, IP33 3YB, England.
Music Sales Pty Limited
20 Resolution Drive, Caringbah, NSW 2229, Australia.

Order No. AM91754
ISBN 0-7119-3892-X
This book © Copyright 2004 by Wise Publications.

Music arranged by Derek Jones.
Music processed by Paul Ewers Music Design.
Printed in the United Kingdom by Caligraving Limited, Thetford, Norfolk.

www.musicsales.com

Somewhere Only We Know

Words & Music by Tim Rice-Oxley, Tom Chaplin & Richard Hughes

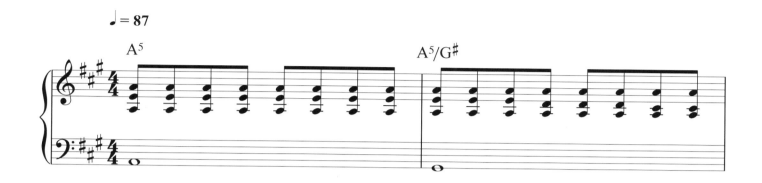

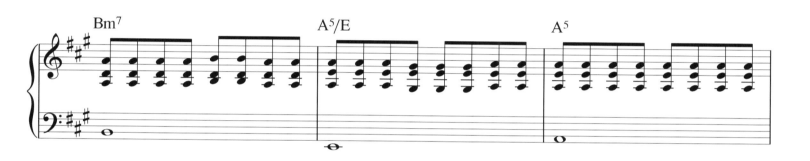

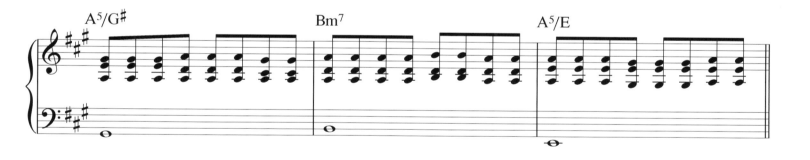

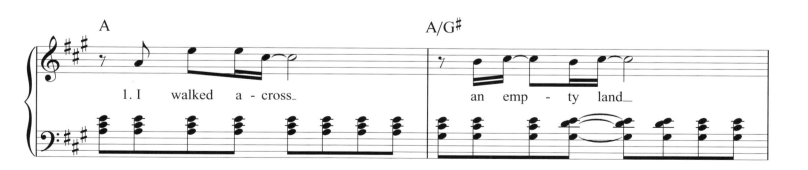

1. I walked a-cross an emp-ty land

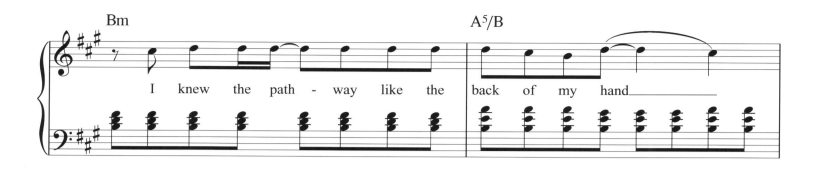

I knew the path - way like the back of my hand

I felt the earth be - neath my feet sat by the riv - er and it

made me com - plete. Oh sim - ple thing, where have you gone?

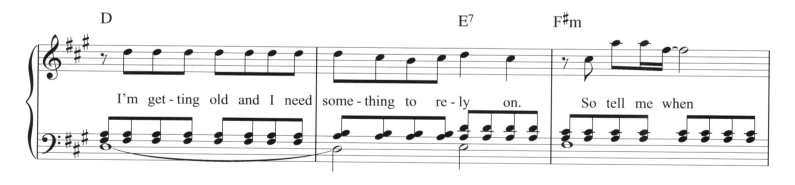

I'm get - ting old and I need some - thing to re - ly on. So tell me when

you're gon - na let me in. I'm get - ting tired and I need some - where to be - gin.

8

Bend And Break

Words & Music by Tim Rice-Oxley, Tom Chaplin & Richard Hughes

light._____ If on - ly I don't

suf - - fo - cate_____ I'll meet you in the

morn - ing when you wake. wake.

Everybody's Changing

Words & Music by Tim Rice-Oxley, Tom Chaplin & Richard Hughes

1. You say___ you wan - der___ your own

2.You're

D.S. al Coda

Coda

rit.

Ev - 'ry-bo - dy's chang - ing and__ I don't feel__ the same.__

17

Your Eyes Open

Words & Music by Tim Rice-Oxley, Tom Chaplin & Richard Hughes

She Has No Time

Words & Music by Tim Rice-Oxley, Tom Chaplin, Richard Hughes & James Sanger

Lone - - ly peo - - ple

tum - ble down - wards and my heart

op - ens up to you when she

time.

25

Can't Stop Now

Words & Music by Tim Rice-Oxley, Tom Chaplin & Richard Hughes

We Might As Well Be Strangers

Words & Music by Tim Rice-Oxley, Tom Chaplin & Richard Hughes

Sunshine

Words & Music by Tim Rice-Oxley, Tom Chaplin, Richard Hughes & James Sanger

This Is The Last Time

Words & Music by Tim Rice-Oxley, Tom Chaplin, Richard Hughes & James Sanger

things they go a-way, but they nev-er do.___ Some-thing
some things nev-er die, well I tried and I tried.___

I was-n't sure___ of___ but I was in the mid-dle of, some-thing

I for-get___ now___ but I've seen too lit-tle of. The

last time you fall on___ me for a-ny-thing you like.___ Your

one last line, you fall on___ me for a-ny-thing you like.___ And

37

Untitled I

Words & Music by Tim Rice-Oxley, Tom Chaplin & Richard Hughes

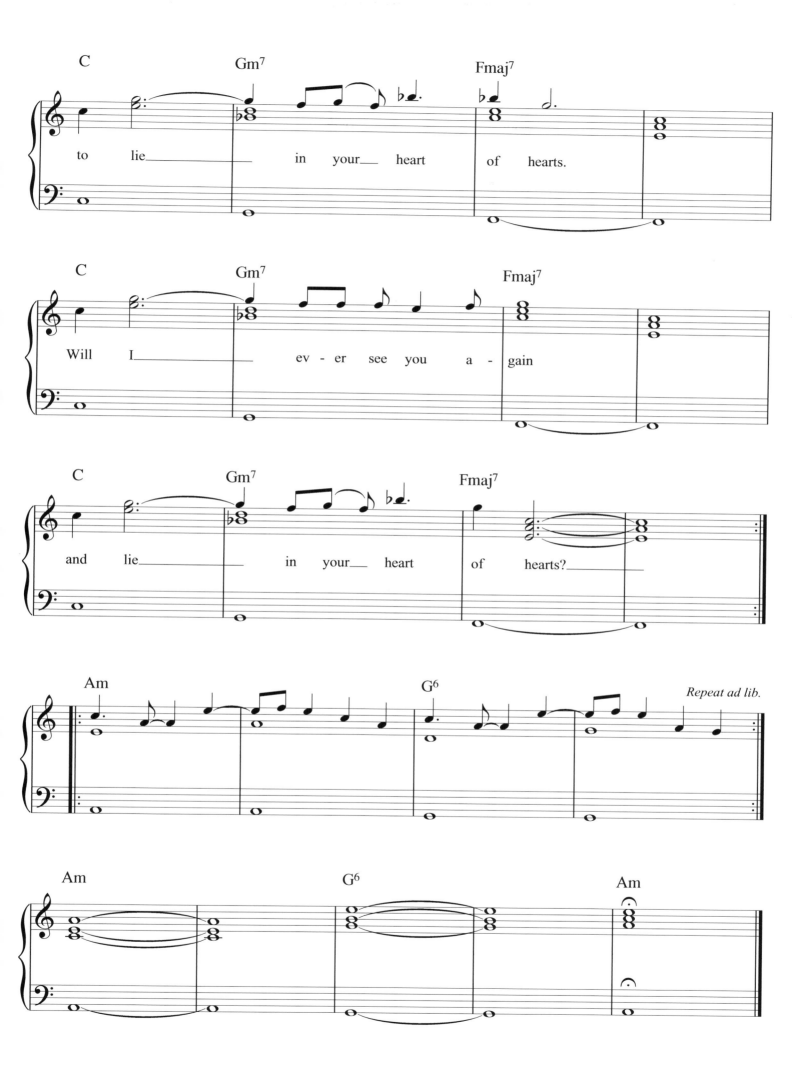

On A Day Like Today

Words & Music by Tim Rice-Oxley, Tom Chaplin & Richard Hughes

wrong turns. If you on - ly___ knew___ the

way I feel,___ I'd real - ly love to tell you but I___

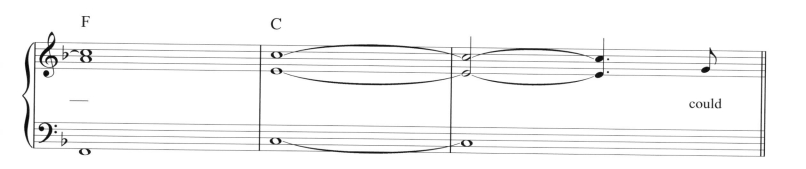

___ could

nev - er seem to say___ the things I need - ed to.

On a day like to - day___ no

F   C   Dm

—   I can't find_____   words to say___ and

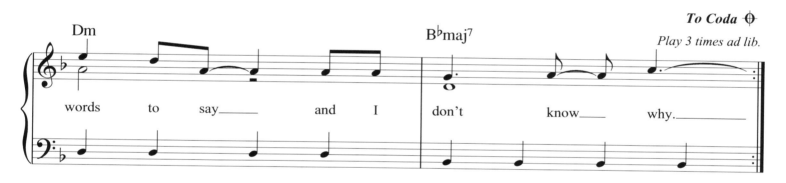

B♭maj⁷   F   C

I don't know__ why_____   I can't find___ the

To Coda ⊕

Play 3 times ad lib.

Dm   B♭maj⁷

words to say_____ and I   don't know___ why._____

F   C   Dm   *D.S. al Coda*

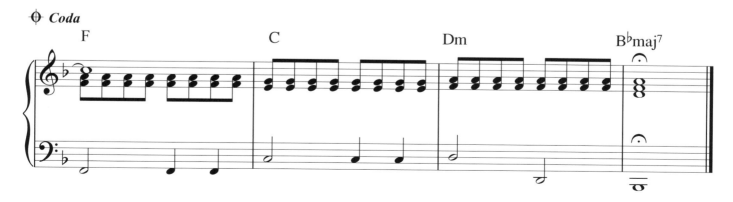

⊕ *Coda*

F   C   Dm   B♭maj⁷

Bedshaped

Words & Music by Tim Rice-Oxley, Tom Chaplin, Richard Hughes & James Sanger

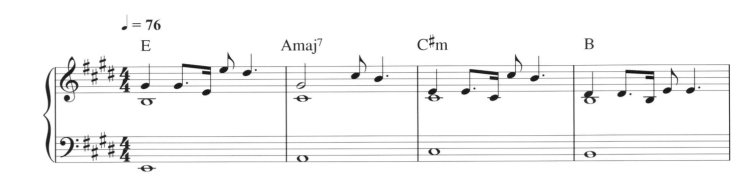

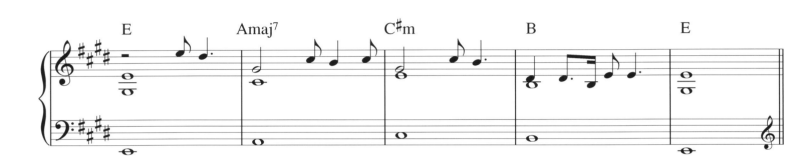

1.Ma - ny's the time I ran with you down the

(2.)know you think I'm hold - ing you down and

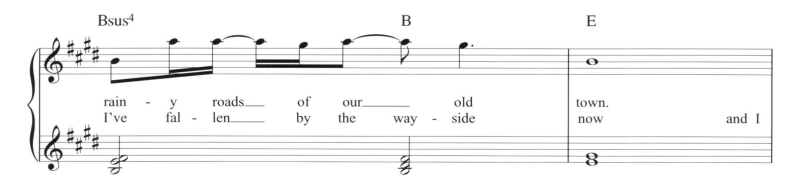

rain - y roads of our old town.

I've fal - len by the way - side now and I